all Hazel

Books by Ted Key

Hazel

Here's Hazel

If You Like Hazel

Many Happy Returns

So'm I

Hazel Rides Again

Fasten Your Seat Belts!

Phyllis

Ted Key's all Hazel

E. P. DUTTON & COMPANY, INC.

The individual cartoons have been previously published and Copyright as follows:
By The Curtis Publishing Company in *The Saturday Evening Post*: 1953, P.
69; 1954, P. 76; 1955, P. 15, 16, 18, 20, 26, 29, 48, 50, 52, 53, 54, 55, 56,
57, 59, 60, 61, 63, 66, 67, 68, 70, 71, 72, 77, 82, 85, 89, 90, 93; 1956, P. End
Papers, Title Page, 10, 14, 17, 23, 27, 30, 31, 32, 35, 37, 38, 40, 41, 44, 45,
46, 47, 49, 50, 51, 53, 55, 57, 58, 62, 64, 65, 69, 72, 75, 76, 83, 87, 89, 91;
1957, P. 12, 15, 19, 21, 22, 24, 25, 28, 30, 33, 34, 36, 38, 39, 42, 43, 48, 51,
54, 67, 70, 73, 74, 78, 79, 80, 83, 84, 86, 87, 88, 91, 93; 1958, P. 11, 13, 23,
74, 80, 81, 92.

Library of Congress Catalog Card Number: 58-9595

TO
MADRE

"For me?"

"Looks like we've got to invite forty-eight to the party."

"How many?"

". . . twenty-four to the party."

"Bingo!"

"Having trouble?"

"The strike zone lies between the shoulders and the . . ."

"Nothing for you."

"YES?"

"Who dragged that in?"

"Good night, Mrs. Walker, good night,
Mr. Walker, Good night Mrs. . . ."

"She's eaten. Don't give her a thing."

"Your dad's napping."

"I presume it has anti-freeze."

"Dinner is SERVED!"

23

"You gave it to 'em, brother!"

"As we took leave of beautiful Yellowstone."

"Roger and over."

"NO!"

"N-O!"

"We are SERVING—if you'll pardon
the expression—LUNCH."

"Must've cleaned the attic."

"You mind?"

". . . and that's why we have a Thanksgiving."

"Compliments of the house."

"They were paying for this when I was a kid."

"On the double!"

"And so, from the starlight roof of the Ritz, we bid fond adieu to . . ."

"How's business?"

"Fill 'er up?"

"Lady . . ."

"For you, Elvis."

"It's your anniversary."

"Louder. We can hear the dialogue."

"Till we return from the shore. Now every
morning, give her three bowls of . . ."

"... thereby giving you that extra power."

"Now what!"

"A product which sells itself. We feel, madam . . ."

"Over here!"

"When who should I run into, as big as life . . ."

". . . dry socks, dry pants, dry shirt, and dry! . . ."

Ted Key

"Relax."

"Any time YOU'RE ready, Casanova."

"Look, friend . . ."

"Forgot his homework."

"Her Serene Highness . . . !"

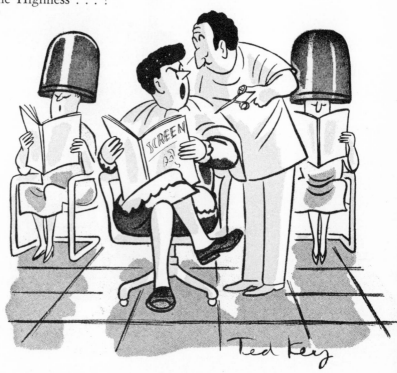

"I can do without the yak-yak."

"What else for dinner besides lamb chops?"

"Let's get this show on the road."

"...and a three and a four..."

"We're next!"

"What we call louse-it-yourself."

". . . The FOLLOWING schools will remain open—
Lowell, Cromwell, East Valley, Emerson . . ."

"Time out!"

"Any time, Lindbergh."

"Going someplace?"

"One moment."

"Truman routs Dewey, re-elected by . . ."

"Now today, because your den mother's indisposed I . . ."

53

"Pond's frozen."

"M-A-R-C-S. Or, spelled backwards . . ."

"That's GALLUP'S opinion, in my opinion . . ."

"What we call a hanger."

"HURRY, HURRY, HURRY!"

"Now the way they vaccinated in those days . . ."

"Repeat that."

"Running short?"

"Don't move."

"O.K.—everybody back out that door."

"I said everybody."

"Any message?"

"You know nothing, of course, about this gum."

"WAFFLES."

"Someone important?"

"Care to know what he pays in taxes?"

"Hot enough for you?"

"Out of chocolate."

"Because it's HIS house, that's why."

"Yes?"

"NOTHING TODAY!!"

"Nice going, William Tell."

"You three should get acquainted."

"Next."

"When it reaches six and a half, SELL."

"Coming through."

"How was Mexico?"

"Found her."

"Earth to Venus. Your soup's getting cold."

"Too Gooey."

"Now here's what we want done . . ."

1

"Nope!"

2

"Nope!"

3

"Nope!"

4

"Yep!"

"Because he has homework."

"Then what happened?"

"Comfy?"

"You always light the filtered end?"

"I said reach, pardner!"

"I'ma reachin!"

"We're running low on friends."

"Greetings."

"Think of it this way— where would YOU be if YOU were a belt?"

"Never mind why not!"

"Where's Do-it-yourself?"

"The car."

"A word with the manager . . ."

"Any nibbles?"

"Hammock's shot."

"It's for you."

Ted Key

"The face is familiar."

"Want yours now?"

"He kidding?"

"Warm enough for you?"

". . . pound of butter and a dozen eggs
and a head of lettuce and . . ."

"Defrosting?"

"School out?"